DC UNIVERSE

SUPER HEROES

Ready for Action!

LONDON, NEW YORK, MUNICH,
MELBOURNE, AND DELHI

Senior Editor Victoria Taylor
Designer Sandra Perry
Senior Designer Anna Formanek
Design Manager Nathan Martin
Managing Editor Laura Gilbert
Publishing Manager Julie Ferris
Publishing Director Simon Beecroft
Pre-production Producer Rebecca Fallowfield
Producer Melanie Mikellides
Jacket Designer Jon Hall

First published in Great Britain in 2013 by
Dorling Kindersley Limited
80 Strand, London, WC2R 0RL

13 14 15 16 17 10 9 8 7 6 5

016 – 187445 – Feb/13

Published in Great Britain by Dorling Kindersley Limited

A catalogue record for this book is available
from the British Library.

ISBN 978-1-40936-613-3

Colour reproduction by Media Development and Printing, UK
Printed and bound in Slovakia by TBB

Discover more at
www.dk.com
www.LEGO.com

Contents

Ready for Action!

Written by Victoria Taylor

Super Heroes

The world is protected by a special group of super heroes.

Batman

Robin

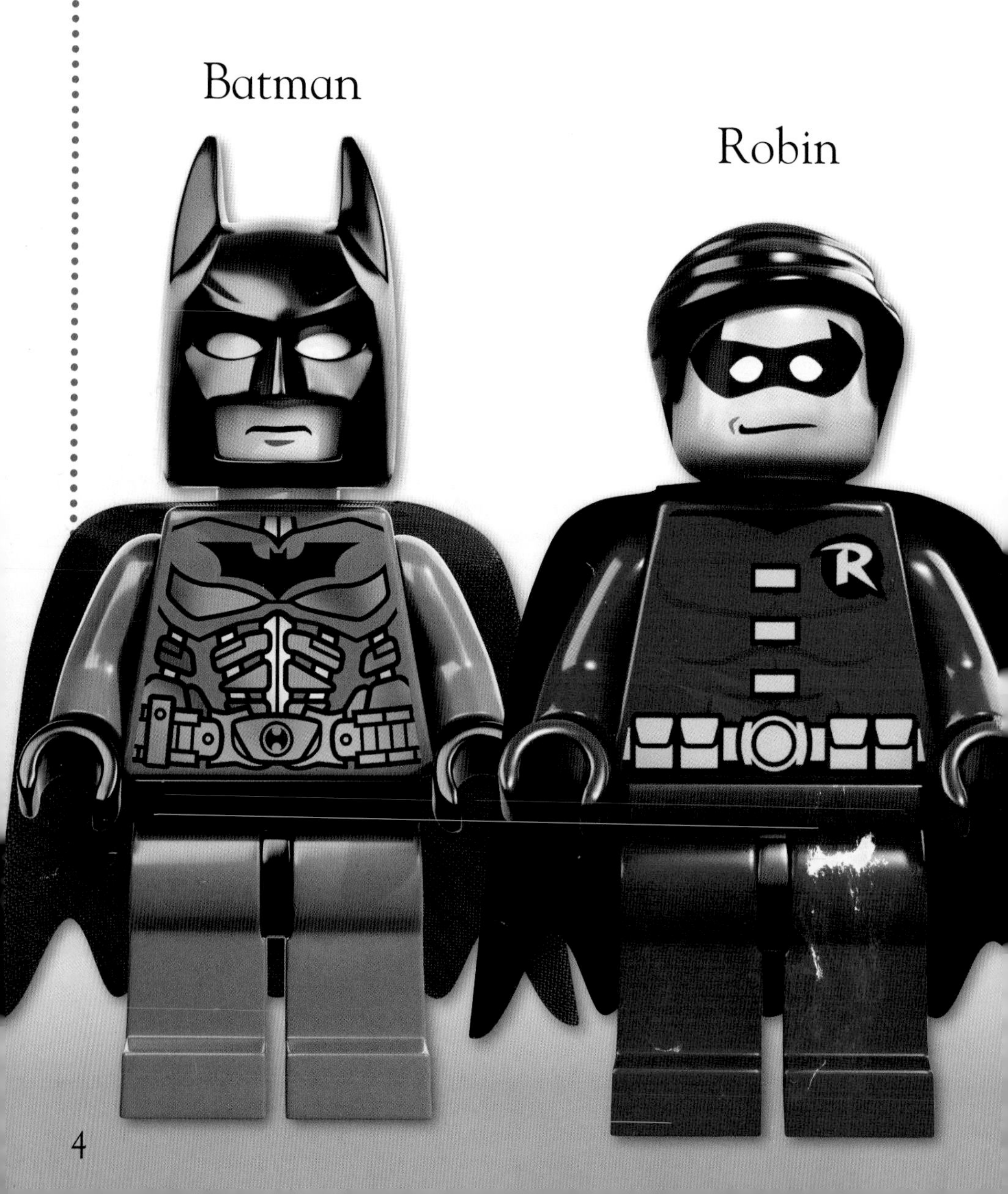

Come and meet some of the super heroes and see them in action. . .

Wonder Woman

Superman

Superman

This is Superman!

He can fly and has super-strength which gives him great power.

He keeps the city of Metropolis safe from villains.

cape

Wonder Woman

This is Wonder Woman!

She is very strong and very fast.

She has a secret weapon. It is a Lasso of Truth that makes criminals confess.

Robot Battle

Superman and Wonder Woman team up to defeat the villain Lex Luthor.

Lex Luthor is Superman's main enemy. The villain has a robot that he can sit inside and control.

Together Superman and Wonder Woman defeat the robot.

Bruce Wayne

This is Bruce Wayne!

Most people think that Bruce is just rich and famous.

But Bruce leads an exciting double-life as the super hero Batman!

Bruce's butler Alfred

Come and meet Batman. . .

Batman

Batman protects the people of Gotham City from dangerous super-villains.

He wears a bullet-proof Batsuit that keeps him safe.

Batsuit

Robin

Batman does not battle Gotham City's crime alone. He has a partner called Robin.

Batman and Robin always look out for each other.

BANE
LOADING
MISSILES
POWER

The Batcave

Welcome to the Batcave! This is a secret cave hidden under Batman's home.

He stores his vehicles here. There is lots of equipment to help Batman fight crime.

The Batmobile

This is the Batmobile. It is Batman's favourite vehicle. The Batmobile is very fast.

It can fire missiles at Batman's enemies. Let's see it in action…

The Two-Face Chase

Batman is in his Batmobile.

He sees villain Two-Face driving away from the bank with a safe!

Batman catches the crook and returns the safe to the bank where it belongs!

The Batwing

This is the Batwing.
It is Batman's super-fast
aeroplane.

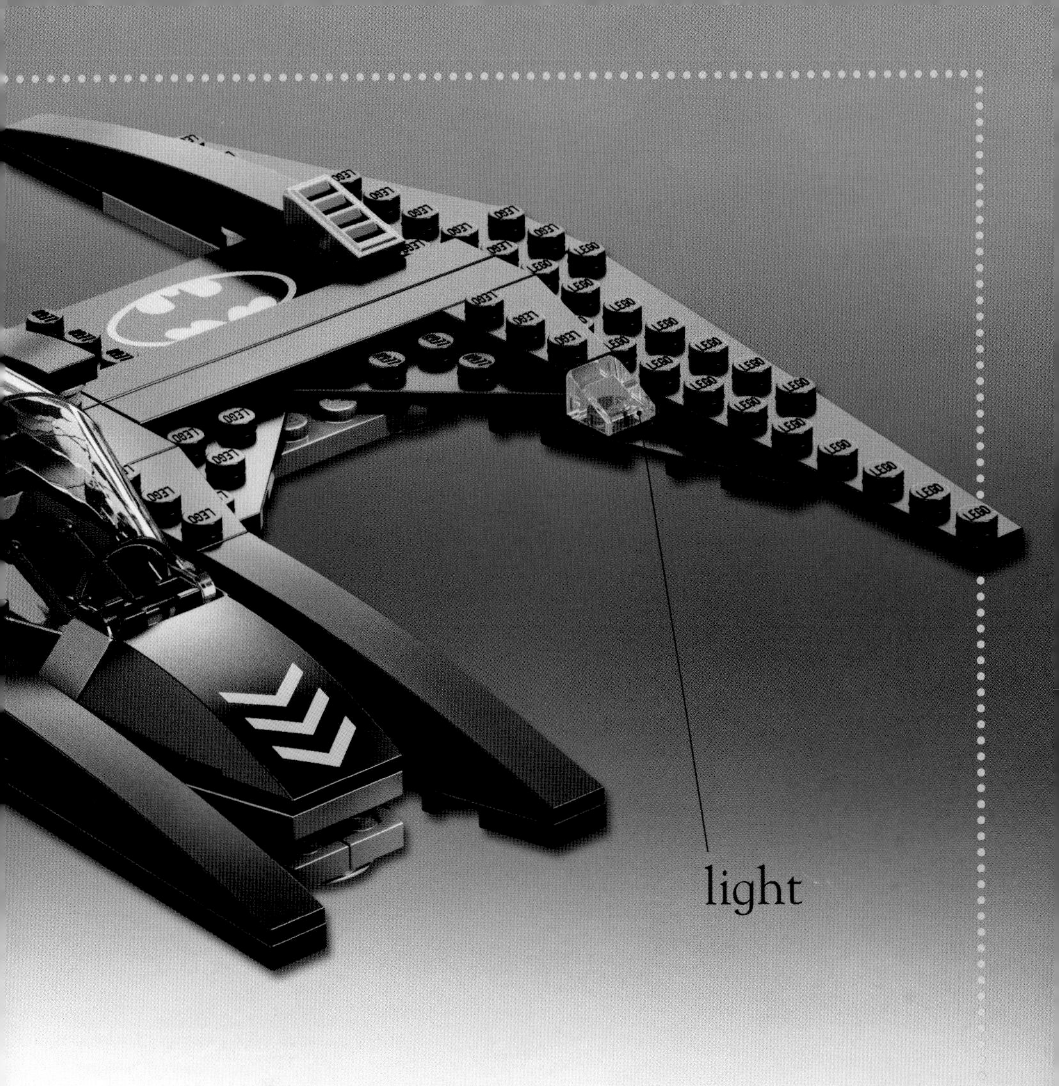

He uses it to defend Gotham City from the air.

Let's see it in action. . .

Batwing over Gotham

The Joker is attacking Gotham City from the sky.

Batman arrives in his Batwing.

The Joker says he will let off toxic laughing gas.

Batman fires missiles at the Joker's helicopter to stop him.

Catcycle Chase

Catwoman has stolen a diamond.
She is escaping on her motorbike.

Batman flies in and throws his Batarang. It knocks the jewel out of Catwoman's hand.

Catwoman is no match for Batman!

Batarang

Funhouse Escape

Three villains have caught Robin and trapped him in the Funhouse fairground ride. Can you see Robin?

Batman arrives in his Batcycle!

He rescues Robin and restores law and order to Gotham City.

A super hero has saved the day again!

Glossary

Batarang
A weapon in the shape of a bat.

Batsuit
The special armoured suit that Batman wears.

lasso
A rope with a loop at the end.

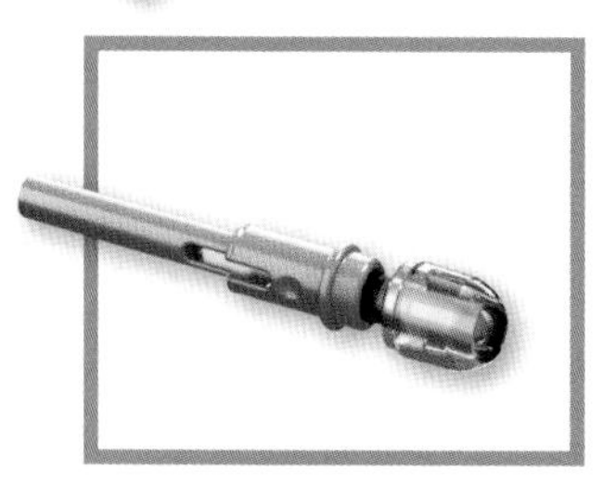

missile
An object that is shot at something.

safe
A strong metal box for storing valuable things.